STRANGER THINGS

THE OTHER SIDE

NETFLIX

STRANGER THINGS

THE OTHER SIDE

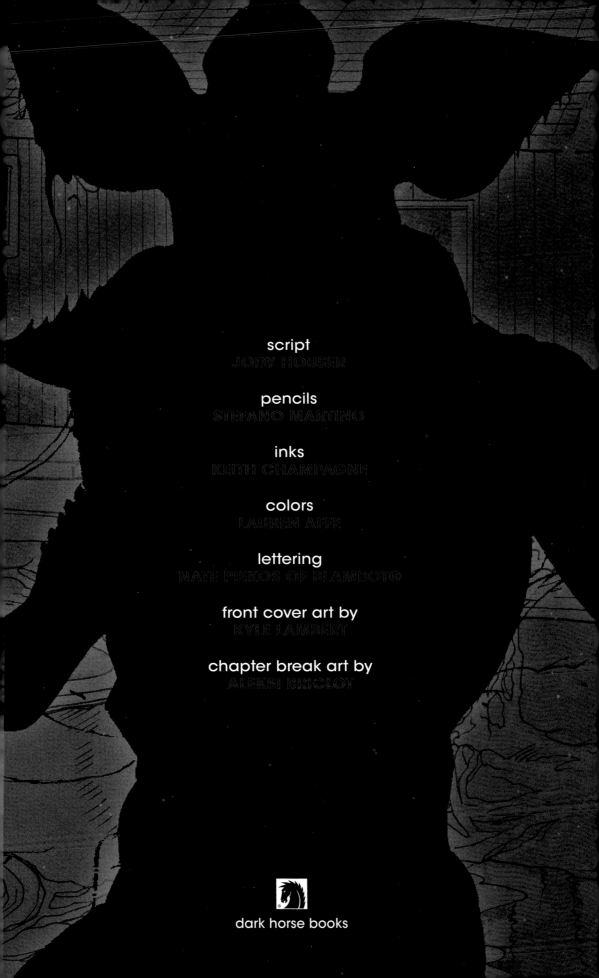

script
JODY HOUSER

pencils
STEFANO MARTINO

inks
KEITH CHAMPAGNE

colors
LAUREN AFFE

lettering
NATE PIEKOS OF BLAMBOT©

front cover art by
KYLE LAMBERT

chapter break art by
ALEKSI BRICLOT

dark horse books

president and publisher
MIKE RICHARDSON

editor
SPENCER CUSHING

assistant editor
KONNER KNUDSEN

collection designer
PATRICK SATTERFIELD

digital art technician
ALLYSON HALLER

Special thanks to KEVIN BURKHALTER, KYLE LAMBERT,
and NETFLIX, including: SHANNON SCHRAM, ELLEN DENG, JESS RICHARDSON, and TARA SINCLAIR.

Advertising Sales: (503) 905-2315 | ComicShopLocator.com

This volume collects issues #1 through #4 of the Dark Horse comic-book series
Stranger Things: The Other Side.

Published by Dark Horse Books
A division of Dark Horse Comics LLC.
10956 SE Main Street
Milwaukie, OR 97222

DarkHorse.com | Netflix.com

First edition: May 2019 | ISBN 978-1-50671-341-0

1 3 5 7 9 10 8 6 4 2
Printed in China

NEIL HANKERSON executive vice president • TOM WEDDLE chief financial officer • RANDY STRADLEY
vice president of publishing • NICK McWHORTER chief business development officer • MATT
PARKINSON vice president of marketing • DALE LAFOUNTAIN vice president of Information technology
CARA NIECE vice president of production and scheduling • MARK BERNARDI vice president of book
trade and digital sales • KEN LIZZI general counsel • DAVE MARSHALL editor in chief • DAVEY ESTRADA
editorial director • CHRIS WARNER senior books editor • CARY GRAZZINI director of specialty projects
LIA RIBACCHI art director • VANESSA TODD-HOLMES director of print purchasing • MATT DRYER
director of digital art and prepress • MICHAEL GOMBOS senior director of licensed publications
KARI YADRO director of custom programs • KARI TORSON director of international licensing

IN THE WORLD OF THE GAME, WILL THE WISE CALLED UPON THE ARCANE ARTS IN HIS BATTLE AGAINST EVIL.

IT WASN'T ENOUGH TO SAVE HIM.

WHERE IS IT? **WHAT** IS IT?

SKRRRRR

SO INTENT ON THE FEARSOME MONSTER AT HIS HEELS, WILL BYERS NEVER REALIZED...

...TEETH AND CLAWS WEREN'T THE ONLY DANGERS THAT HE FACED.

CAST A PROTECTION SPELL!

THE MONSTER LOOMING OVER THE BOY IS A STRANGE ECHO OF THE STORY THAT PLAYED OUT A SHORT TIME AGO.

FIREBALL HIM!

CAST PROTECTION!

IN THE REAL WORLD, WILL DOESN'T HAVE A CHOICE OF SPELLS.

FIREBALL!

THE QUESTION OF WHETHER THIS **IS** THE REAL WORLD OR NOT REMAINS.

PROTECTION!

MADE IT!

LIGHTS AREN'T WORKING?

click

THAT FLASH BEFORE...DID A CIRCUIT BLOW?

MOM? JONATHAN?

MOM MUST BE WORKING LATE AGAIN.

AND JONATHAN PROBABLY TOOK HIS CAMERA OUT.

WHATEVER'S GOING ON, THEY'LL KNOW WHAT TO DO WHEN THEY GET HOME.

click

THEY'LL FIND ME.

AS HE WAITS, THE ADRENALINE FROM THE CHASE DRAINS AWAY.

HE MAY NOT YET BE SAFE...

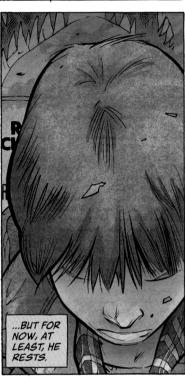

...BUT FOR NOW, AT LEAST, HE RESTS.

JESUS.

MAN, THE DICE *HATE* YOU.

THIS SUCKS. OUR MAGIC-USER IS SO *WEAK!*

WE'RE GONNA *DIE*, WE'RE GONNA DIE *SO* FAST.

MAYBE HE SHOULD HAVE PICKED A *DIFFERENT* CLASS...

ANYTHING IN THE RULES ABOUT REROLLING WHEN MAKING CHARACTERS?

NO. *FATE* HAS ALREADY SPOKEN. THE PARTY HAS BEEN *GATHERED*.

NO REROLLS.

YOU TWO ACT LIKE THE DICE GAVE YOU *SO* MUCH MORE POWER THAN HIM.

YOU'RE *BOTH* STILL LEVEL ONE. *EASY* PREY.

AND IF SOMETHING EATS YOU, *DON'T* BLAME WILL THE WISE.

IT ISN'T A *CONTEST* TO SEE WHICH OF YOU IS THE STRONGEST OR CAN GET THE MOST KILLS.

YOU *LIVE* AS A PARTY OR YOU *DIE* ALONE.

"THE ONLY WAY YOU SURVIVE AND LEVEL UP IS *TOGETHER*."

AHH!

FELL ASLEEP...BUT IT'S STILL DARK OUT?

AND IT STILL SMELLS TERRIBLE.

FOR THE FIRST TIME, WILL *REALLY* SEES THROUGH THE STRANGENESS THAT SURROUNDS HIM.

IT'S NOT THAT HIS HOME HAS BEEN INFECTED BY SOMETHING.

HELLO? ANYBODY HERE?

IT'S THAT HE WAS NEVER ACTUALLY HOME AT ALL.

≤KAFF≥

THE FIRST TRUTH HE LEARNED ABOUT ADVENTURING STILL STANDS.

THE PARTY THAT FIGHTS TOGETHER SURVIVES TOGETHER.

SPLITTING THE PARTY CAN HAVE DISASTROUS CONSEQUENCES.

AFTER ALL, ON THEIR OWN, AN ADVENTURER IS THE **EASIEST** OF PREY.

THERE HAS TO BE A WAY BACK...

THEN HE SEES IT. THE FIRST HINTS OF LIGHT IN THIS PLACE, LIKE A MEMORY ETCHED INTO THE DARK.

CASTLE BYERS

AND WITH THE LIGHT COMES VOICES, SOUNDING OUT FROM SPEAKERS TOO DISTANT TO SEE. AMONG THE TREES...AND YET NOT.

WILL

WILL BYERS

ARE YOU

WILL

H-HELLO?

IF SOMEONE IS INDEED SEARCHING FOR HIM, IT ISN'T IN THIS STRANGE SHADOW OF THE MIRKWOOD.

BUT THEN--

OVER THERE!

HELLO?!

IS SOMEBODY--

IN THEIR CAMPAIGNS, MIKE THE DUNGEON MASTER OFTEN PLAYS CHARACTERS THE PARTY ENCOUNTERS ON THEIR JOURNEY.

Spirit of the wood! I have been led astray! Do you know the path back to my companions?

FIGURES TO SET THEM ON THEIR NEXT QUEST, OR TO OFFER THE INFORMATION THEY REQUIRE. SOMEONE TO LIGHT THE WAY.

Brave traveler, the Mirkwood is no place for you. Let me be your guide to--

HOWEVER, AS WILL HAS ALREADY LEARNED, THIS IS HARDLY A GAME.

H-HELLO?

21

HIS ALL-TOO-BRIEF HOPE FADES AWAY, SAVE ONE SMALL KERNEL. SHE SAW HIM. **SOMEONE** SAW HIM.

SOMEONE IS LOOKING FOR HIM.

WILL BYERS

WILL

WHERE ARE YOU

BUT HOW TO **REACH** THEM IS ANOTHER QUESTION ENTIRELY.

WILL

WILL

WILL

WHATEVER THE ANSWER, HE KNOWS IT WON'T BE FOUND ON MIRKWOOD.

I WONDER...

HELLO? CAN ANYONE HEAR ME?

JUST BECAUSE IT WORKED IN A MOVIE DOESN'T MEAN IT WILL **HERE**, MORON.

BUT I DO KNOW HOW I TALK TO PEOPLE OUT THERE...

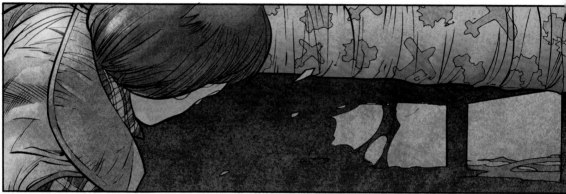

IT'S BEEN YEARS SINCE WILL FEARED WHAT MIGHT BE LURKING UNDER HIS BED.

BUT HERE, NOW? THOSE NIGHTMARES ARE BROUGHT INTO SHARP RELIEF, CARVED INTO HIS BRAIN AS IF THEY NEVER REALLY LEFT.

BRAVERY CAN BE A FRIEND IN THE MOMENT.

BUT IT DOESN'T ALWAYS TAKE INTO ACCOUNT THE LONG TERM.

THE BOY THINKS ONLY OF GETTING THROUGH THE ENEMY IN FRONT OF HIM. GETTING BACK TO WHERE HE BELONGS.

...AND NOT ABOUT CONSERVING AMMUNITION.

31

MOM? CAN YOU HEAR ME?!

ANYBODY?!

CAN YOU GUYS HEAR ME AT *ALL?*

...OVER.

I'M SOMEPLACE THAT *LOOKS* LIKE HOME. BUT IT'S NOT. IT'S...

I'M SORRY, WILL. OUR HOUSE IS JUST TOO FAR OUT.

"I DON'T THINK YOUR FRIENDS CAN HEAR YOU FROM HERE."

IT'S OKAY, MOM. THERE'S LOTS OF PLACES WE CAN ALL USE THEM.

HE WAITS FOR TIME INDETERMINATE. BUT THERE IS NO REPLY. NO CONNECTION.

NO WAY TO WARN THE WORLD ABOUT THE MONSTER IN THE WALLS.

NO WAY TO ASK FOR HELP.

MOM DOESN'T **HAVE A** SUPERCOMM.

AT LEAST, NOT YET.

SO HOW WAS SHE TALKING TO ME BEFORE?

SHHHHH

SHHHHHCK--ILL, IT'S--SHHHHH

H-- HELLO

NOT AS CLEAR AS THE SUPERCOMM WAS, BUT IT SOUNDS LIKE...

SHHHCK--TO ME--SHHHHHCK-- HERE--SHHHCK-- WHERE YOU ARE, HON--

SHHHCK-- HEAR YOU. PLEASE--

MOM!

SHHHHHHH HHHHHHH HHHH

SHHCCCK!

AAAH!

MOM?!

SILENCE IS HIS ONLY ANSWER.

SO HE GOES BACK TO THE LAST PLACE HE HEARD HER VOICE. LOUDER, CLEARER.

INTENT ON HIS DESTINATION, HE FAILS TO NOTICE THE HINTS OF LIGHT THAT APPEAR...

...ALMOST AS IF FOLLOWING HIM.

MOM, IT'S ME! CAN YOU HEAR--

HE GETS AN ANSWER. BUT NOT THE ONE HE EXPECTS.

♪♫ DARLING YOU

IT'S NOT TURNING. BUT I CAN HEAR...

♫ STAY OR

IT'S FAINT, LIKE THE VOICES IN THE WOODS.

AM I HEARING IT FROM MY REAL ROOM?

♫♫ YOU SAY

CAN ANYONE HEAR ME?!

♪♫ I'LL BE HERE

♫♫ LET ME KNOW

SKRRR

♫ SHOULD I GO?

AND FINALLY...
SILENCE.

I THINK IT'S GONE. FOR NOW...

MAYBE IF I HEAD FURTHER OUT, I CAN PICK SOMETHING UP.

THIS IS WILL BYERS. CAN ANYONE READ ME?

WHICH STREET IS--

AAAAAAHHHHH!

"YOU HEAR SCREAMS."

THEY SOUND LIKE THEY'RE COMING FROM THE VILLAGE DOWN THE ROAD. BUT YOU CAN'T TELL ANYTHING BEYOND THAT.

WHAT DO YOU DO?

THAT TRADER *DID* SAY THERE WERE RUMORS OF A DEVIL SWINE IN THE FOREST.

I USED ALL MY SPELLS AGAINST THAT WOOD GOLEM...

WE NEED TO REST FIRST. WE CAN'T HELP *ANYONE* IF WE GET KILLED OURSELVES.

WE CAN'T JUST LEAVE PEOPLE WHO ARE IN TROUBLE.

I'M NOT SAYING WE LEAVE *FOREVER*, BUT WE NEED TO BE AT FULL STRENGTH. DEVIL SWINE ARE BAD NEWS.

I DON'T WANT INNOCENT PEOPLE TO GET EATEN BY DEVIL SWINE.

BUT I DON'T WANT *US* TO GET EATEN EITHER...

FIGURE IT OUT, GUYS.

JUST REMEMBER...

HELLO? IS ANYONE--

ARE THESE FROM THE GIRL WHO SCREAMED?

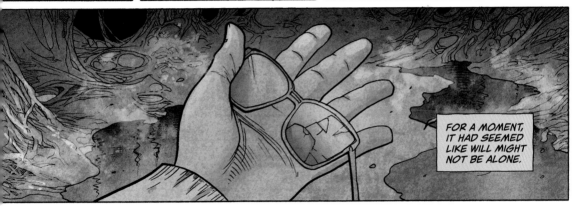

FOR A MOMENT, IT HAD SEEMED LIKE WILL MIGHT NOT BE ALONE.

BUT HIS HOPES ARE DASHED. AND HE'S NOT SURE WHICH IS WORSE.

THAT HE WASN'T ABLE TO SAVE SOMEONE WHO NEEDED HELP...

...OR THAT SOME SMALL SLIVER OF HIM IS GLAD THAT HE WASN'T THE PREY.

LITTLE DOES HE REALIZE THAT A PATH HAS BEEN LAID TO HIM IN LIGHT.

THAT HE ISN'T NEARLY AS ALONE AS HE THINKS.

WILL...

...ARE YOU HERE?

ARE YOU SAFE?

I NEED TO KNOW WHERE TO FIND YOU, HONEY.

WHERE... WHERE ARE YOU?

I DON'T KNOW! I DON'T--

AND I DON'T KNOW HOW TO GET BACK! YOU HAVE TO COME FIND ME!

CAN YOU...

CAN YOU TELL ME WHERE YOU ARE? CAN YOU--

MOM...

THE ONLY ANSWER HE CAN GIVE HER IS NO. AND HE CAN'T BRING HIMSELF TO DO THAT TO HER.

TO HIMSELF.

TWO WORDS, UNTHINKABLE ONLY MOMENTS AGO, JUST AREN'T ENOUGH.

PLEASE BABY. I NEED TO FIND YOU.

TELL ME WHAT TO DO.

PLEASE JUST...

WILL...

44

"RIGHT HERE."

"RIGHT HERE."

I'M RIGHT HERE! IN THE FAMILY ROOM! OR A COPY! OR--

...I DON'T KNOW WHAT THAT MEANS...

I DON'T EITHER, MOM!

I DON'T KNOW WHAT TO DO!

...TELL ME WHAT TO DO.

HAVING THE MEANS TO SPEAK ISN'T THE SAME AS HAVING THE RIGHT WORDS.

WHAT SHOULD I DO?

Artist FRUIZ had originally been tapped to help create a pinup piece for our pitch to license *Stranger Things*. We loved working with him so we brought him back to create art for the back cover of each of our first four comic books. Above you can see some of his other ideas for the piece. In addition to the final art, inside this gatefold, you can see work from some of the other artists we partnered with when building the pitch to Netflix.

SOME TIME AGO...

THERE HAS TO BE A BETTER WAY TO TALK TO PEOPLE IN THE REAL WORLD.

I COULD HEAR MOM, BEFORE THE MONSTER CAME. BUT SHE COULDN'T HEAR ME.

BUT I THINK SHE *DID* HEAR ME ONCE, AT LEAST A LITTLE, WITH THE SUPERCOMM.

MAYBE IF I CAN GET IN RANGE...

IS THAT THE GUYS?

HE HAD COME TO HIS FRIEND'S HOME, OR SOME SHADE OF IT, TO SPEAK TO THE OTHER SIDE.

MM M MMM MMMM MM M

NOW, THE REAL WORLD WAS SPEAKING BACK.

...SEARCH FOR THE...WILL BYERS...TRAGIC END TODAY...

AND WHAT IT HAD TO SAY FILLED HIM WITH HORROR TO HIS VERY MARROW.

NO...

"...BYERS' BODY...FOUND IN THE WATER...BY...POLICE EARLIER THIS...

"...IT WAS...BY..."

BUT MOM KNOWS! SHE WAS JUST *TALKING* TO ME!

MOM!

MOM! CAN YOU HEAR ME?!

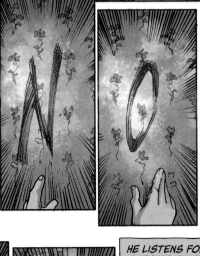

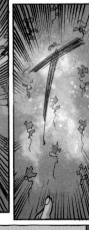

HE LISTENS FOR THE FAINT STRAINS OF HER VOICE. THE QUESTIONS. THE WORRY.

BUT THERE IS ONLY SILENCE.

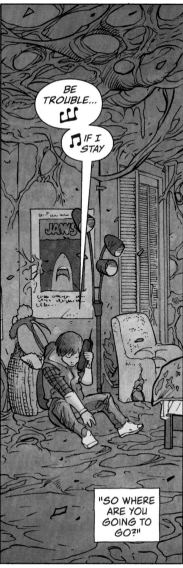

I SAY WE STAY PUT. WE WERE HIRED TO DEFEND THE TOWN.

AND WE NEED MORE SUPPLIES IF WE'RE GOING TO DO THAT!

DO WE KNOW HOW CLOSE THE ARMY IS?

THEY COULD BE HERE IN DAYS. OR THEY COULD BE HERE IN HOURS.

THAT'S NOT HELPFUL.

FINE! I HEAD TOWARDS THE FOREST PATH.

I...I GUESS I'M BACKING HIM UP.

SCREW IT! ME TOO.

THIS IS SUCH A BAD IDEA...

AS YOU MOVE DOWN THE FOREST PATH, THE TREES AROUND YOU ARE QUIET. TOO QUIET.

SHOULD WE TURN BACK?

WE JUST LEFT. WE CAN'T GO BACK ALREADY.

WE CAN'T GO BACK AT ALL IF WE'RE DEAD.

YOU DON'T SEE ANY-THING AS YOU APPROACH A FOREST CLEARING. YOU DON'T HEAR ANYTHING.

BUT YOU CAN'T HELP FEELING LIKE YOU'RE BEING WATCHED...

AW SHIT. IT'S THE ASSASSIN, ISN'T IT?

59

WILL WASN'T SURE WHEN THE MONSTER STOPPED CHASING HIM.

BUT HIS MOTHER HAD TOLD HIM TO HIDE. SO HE DID.

NEVER LINGERING IN ONE PLACE FOR TOO LONG.

RUNNING FROM DEATH, WILL EVENTUALLY FOUND HIMSELF AMONG THE DEAD.

WHAT WAS BURIED IN THE GRAVES OF THIS UNHOLY PLACE, HE DIDN'T KNOW. DIDN'T **WANT** TO KNOW.

BUT CEMETERIES DO MORE THAN JUST HOUSE THE DEAD. THEY OFFER SOLACE TO THE LIVING.

...DO NOT BE DISMAYED...AM YOUR...

THESE WORDS THAT STRETCH BETWEEN WORLDS GIVE HIM COMFORT, RENEW HIS STRENGTH.

...WILL STRENGTHEN YOU...I WILL HELP...

THESE WORDS MAKE HIM BRAVE ENOUGH TO HEAD BACK TO THE DOORWAY HE FOUND...

...ALMOST AS IF THEY WERE SPOKEN JUST FOR HIM.

...UPHOLD... WITH MY RIGHTEOUS...

IT'S TIMES LIKE THESE THAT OUR FAITH IS CHALLENGED.

"HOW, IF HE IS TRULY BENEVOLENT...

"...COULD GOD TAKE FROM US SOMEONE SO YOUNG, SO INNOCENT?

"IT WOULD BE EASY TO TURN AWAY FROM GOD.

"BUT WE MUST REMEMBER THAT NOTHING, NOT EVEN TRAGEDY...

"...CAN SEPARATE US FROM HIS LOVE."

IT'LL BE OKAY. THERE HAS TO BE ANOTHER DOORWAY OUT.

I DIDN'T GET HERE FROM THE LIVING ROOM.

THAT HOUSE WHERE I FOUND THOSE GLASSES...

...IF SOMEONE ELSE CAME IN FROM THERE, MAYBE I CAN--

HE...

...HELP...

THE SIGHT OF A HUMAN FACE, CLEAR AND REAL AND *HERE*, STUNS WILL INTO INACTION FOR A MOMENT.

ONLY FOR A MOMENT.

HE... HELLO? ARE YOU...OKAY?

DALE... HURT BAD...

HUNTING... IN THE WOODS. SOMETHING...SOME-*THING* GRABBED US.

ITS FACE...

HELP... HELP DALE...

I...I WILL. WE'LL ALL GET HOME.

IT'S AN EMPTY PROMISE.

BUT IT DOES ITS WORK.

GUH... GOOD...

I THINK HE'S--

THIS PLACE IS FULL OF HORRORS, BUT SEEING A DEAD BODY IS A NEW ONE FOR WILL.

BUT THIS STRANGER, WHOEVER HE WAS, ISN'T THE ONLY SURPRISE THAT THE WOODS HOLD.

JONATHAN!

JONATHAN, WHERE ARE YOU?!

JONATHAN? THAT'S MY BROTHER'S NAME...

...IS HE HERE? AND WHO'S THAT YELLING?!

THE HELP HE'S BEEN WAITING FOR IS SO CLOSE NOW.

BUT SO IS THE MONSTER. AND THAT KEEPS HIM FROM CALLING OUT.

NANCY! FOLLOW MY VOICE!

IT **IS** JONATHAN! HE'S LOOKING FOR ME!

SHE...SHE'LL NEVER MAKE IT. IT'S TOO FAST.

HAVE TO MAKE SURE SHE GETS OUT FIRST.

TWAK

SKRAAAA!

GOTTA DRAW IT AWAY!

MINUTES AGO, WILL BYERS HAD HOPE.

IT WASN'T THE FIRST TIME HE'D FOUND IT IN THIS STRANGE WORLD. IT WASN'T THE FIRST TIME HE'D LOST IT.

A FAMILIAR FACE, A SOOTHING VOICE IN THE WALL.

LIGHT AND SAFETY SHINING OUT OF A TREE.

NOW THERE IS ONLY DARKNESS AND THE MONSTERS THAT IT HOLDS.

AND HOW LONG HE CAN KEEP ONE STEP AHEAD, HE DOESN'T KNOW.

HE SUSPECTS THAT IT MAY NOT BE FOR MUCH LONGER.

THE AIR... GETTING HARDER TO BREATHE.

THOUGHT I WAS GETTING USED TO IT.

MAYBE I JUST NEED TO REST...

WILL IS AWARE OF TIME PASSING AS HE MOVES THROUGH THE WOODS. OF THINGS CHANGING.

HOW MUCH OF EITHER, THOUGH, HE CAN'T SAY.

THERE IS LESS AND LESS HE'S SURE OF HERE IN THE DARK.

ALL HE KNOWS IS THAT THIS STRANGE WORLD IS GROWING EVEN STRANGER.

AND HIS STRENGTH IS FLAGGING.

WHAT HE SEES BEFORE HIM IS LIKELY A TRICK. EITHER OF THIS PLACE, OR HIS OWN MIND.

FALLING FOR IT WOULDN'T BE VERY WISE AT ALL.

BUT HE HAS FEW OPTIONS NOW. THERE WILL BE NO MORE RUNNING.

THE ONLY WAY HE WILL SURVIVE IS TO FIND SHELTER. A SAFE PLACE.

A HOME AWAY FROM HOME.

YOUR MOM...

...SHE'S COMING FOR YOU.

HURRY.

HURRY.

JUST... JUST HOLD ON A LITTLE LONGER.

THIS PLACE HAS TAKEN EVERYTHING FROM HIM.

ALMOST.

...IF I STAY... ♫

...TROUBLE... ♫♫

THE SONG MAY GIVE HIM STRENGTH, AS IT HAS IN THE PAST.

BUT IT ALSO SERVES AS A BEACON.

AND BY THE TIME HE REALIZES THAT...

...I GO NOW

...IT'S ALREADY TOO LATE.

SKRRRR

SKRRR

NO. IT'S JUST A STUPID BOOK.

I HEARD HIS BOOKS WERE *REALLY* SCARY.

YEAH, BUT THOSE ARE ABOUT MONSTERS AND HORROR STUFF.

THIS ONE'S SUPPOSED TO BE A FANTASY, RIGHT?

I THOUGHT MAYBE I COULD GET SOME COOL IDEAS FOR THE NEXT CAMPAIGN.

MAYBE YOU COULD ASK MISS MARISSA?

YEAH, RIGHT.

SHE'D PROBABLY CALL MY MOM AND TELL HER I WAS READING INAPPROPRIATE STUFF.

WOULD YOU REALLY GET IN TROUBLE FOR JUST *ASKING* ABOUT A BOOK?

WORSE.

MY MOM'S ALL INTO SITTING DOWN AS A *FAMILY* AND TALKING ABOUT OUR *FEELINGS* AND CRAP NOW.

I COULD SNEAK IT INTO MY HOUSE. MY MOM WOULDN'T CARE.

...I DON'T MEAN IT LIKE THAT. OF COURSE SHE *CARES.*

SHE'S JUST REALLY BUSY WORKING EXTRA SHIFTS. I DON'T THINK SHE'D NOTICE.

HEY, YOUR MOM IS PRETTY COOL.

I MEAN, SHE'S STILL A MOM. BUT SHE KIND OF *GETS* IT, YOU KNOW?

YEAH. OR AT LEAST SHE TRIES.

I BET I COULD READ A FEW CHAPTERS BEFORE BABY HOLLY IS DONE WITH STORYTIME.

BESIDES, IF *YOU* READ IT, IT COULD SPOIL THE CAMPAIGN.

YOU GOT ME. I'M JUST LOOKING OUT FOR WILL THE WISE.

THERE IS NO SENSE OF ANYTHING FOR A WHILE. OF TIME OR PLACE OR PEOPLE.

AND WHEN THE WORLD FINALLY RETURNS, IT'S ALMOST TOO BRIGHT TO BE BELIEVED.

HEY.

HI, SWEET-HEART.

HEY, BUDDY.

WHERE...

WHERE AM I?

THE DEMOGORGON.

WE KNOW. IT'S OKAY.

IT'S DEAD.

"WE MADE A NEW FRIEND.

"SHE STOPPED IT.

"SHE SAVED US."

BUT SHE'S GONE NOW.

AND WILL BYERS IS LEFT TO WONDER.

IS IT REALLY OVER?

CAN ANYONE TRULY FACE A DEMOGORGON AND EMERGE UNSCATHED?

Illustration by JEN BARTEL

GERARD WAY

THE UMBRELLA ACADEMY™

Written by **GERARD WAY** / Art by **GABRIEL BÁ** / Featuring covers by **JAMES JEAN**

The seven adopted children of Sir Reginald Hargreeves form the Umbrella Academy, a dysfunctional family of superheroes with bizarre powers. These disgruntled siblings are the only ones who can save the world from robot assassins, fashionable terrorists, and their own worst impulses! Now a live-action series from Netflix!

"It's the X-Men for cool people." —GRANT MORRISON (*ALL STAR SUPERMAN*)

**VOLUME 1:
APOCALYPSE SUITE**
ISBN 978-1-59307-978-9
$17.99

**VOLUME 2:
DALLAS**
ISBN 978-1-59582-345-8
$17.99

**VOLUME 3:
HOTEL OBLIVION**
ISBN 978-1-50671-142-3
COMING SUMMER 2019!

**THE UMBRELLA ACADEMY
JOURNAL**
$19.99
NOV180283

**THE UMBRELLA ACADEMY
"WHEN EVIL RAINS" MUG**
NOV180282
$12.99

**THE UMBRELLA ACADEMY
MAGNET 4-PACK**
$9.99
NOV180279

**THE UMBRELLA ACADEMY
ENAMEL PIN SET**
$14.99
NOV180281

**THE UMBRELLA ACADEMY
COASTER SET**
$9.99
NOV180280

**THE UMBRELLA ACADEMY
PLAYING CARDS**
$4.99
DEC180427

Killjoys
The True Lives of the Fabulous™

Written by **GERARD WAY** & **SHAUN SIMON** / Art by **BECKY CLOONAN** & **DAN JACKSON**

Over a decade ago a team of revolutionaries called the Killjoys lost their lives while saving a mysterious young girl from the tyrannical megacorporation Better Living Industries. Today, the Killjoys live on in memory, if not belief, as BLI widens its reach and freedom fades. The Girl, now grown, reemerges and is put in the spotlight as a savior, a role she knows nothing about. But with the new revolution hell bent on body counts, the Girl must look within herself to put an end to BLI once and for all.

TRADE PAPERBACK
ISBN 978-1-59582-462-2
$19.99

"Uniquely refreshing." —IGN